RISING ★ STARS
ASSESSMENT

Reading

Progress Tests

Year

6

Helen Lewis

Series Advisors: Cornwall Learning

RISING ★ STARS

CORNWALL LEARNING

Rising Stars UK Ltd, 7 Hatchers Mews, Bermondsey Street, London SE1 3GS

www.risingstars-uk.com

First published 2014

Text, design and layout © Rising Stars UK Ltd 2014

All facts are correct at time of going to press. All referenced websites were correct at the time this book went to press.

The right of Helen Lewis to be identified as the author of this work has been asserted by her in accordance with the Copyright, Design and Patents Act 1998.

Author: Helen Lewis
Educational consultants: Shareen Mayers, Sutton Improvement and Support Services, and Sara Moult, Cornwall Learning
Accessibility reviewer: Vivien Kilburn
Editorial: Lesley Densham for Green Desert Ltd and Sarah Davies
Design: Andy Wilson for Green Desert Ltd
Illustrations: David Woodroffe
Photos: (pages 20, 21 and 59) istockphoto.com; (page 58) Macrophage engulfing TB bacteria, SEM, SCIENCE PHOTO LIBRARY
Cover design: Burville-Riley Partnership

Acknowledgements:
pp9–10 extract from *The Sword in the Stone*, a traditional story from the *Tales of King Arthur*, retold by Felicity Brooks, reproduced from Tales of King Arthur by permission of Usborne Publishing, 83–85 Saffron Hill, London EC1N 8RT, UK, www.usborne.com © 2006 Usborne Publishing Ltd; p11 *The Titanic* by Gillian Clarke © Kingfisher 1996; pp18–19 an extract from *The Firework-Maker's Daughter* by Philip Pullman, adapted for the stage by Stephen Russell © Oberon Books Ltd. 2012, adaptation © Stephen Russell, 2010, reprinted by permission of Oberon Books; pp20–21 *Michelangelo*, adapted from the original text on the Ducksters website (www.ducksters.com/biography/artists/michelangelo.php); pp27–28 *Prehistoric Britain*, adapted from *The Usborne History of Britain* by Ruth Brocklehurst © Usborne Publishing 2013; pp29–30 extract from *Carrie's War* by Nina Bawden, adapted for the stage by Emma Reeves © Oberon Books Ltd 2006, adaptation copyright Emma Reeves, 2006, reprinted by permission of Oberon Books; pp37–8 *Barney and the Chalk Pit*, an extract from the first chapter of *Stig of the Dump* by Clive King © Puffin Classics 2010; pp39–40, *Talking Turkeys* by Benjamin Zephaniah © Puffin 1995; p47 *Geography Lesson* from Selected Poems by Brian Patten © Rogers, Coleridge & White, Literary Agents 2007; pp48–9 *The Creature in the Sand*, an extract from *Five Children and It* by E. Nesbit © Wildside Press 2005; pp56–7 extract from the first chapter of *Kensuke's Kingdom* by Michael Morpurgo © Heinemann Young Books Ltd 1999; pp58–9 *Being Human*, an extract from *Why Is Snot Green? And Other Extremely Important Questions (And Answers) from the Science Museum* by Glen Murphy © 2007 Macmillan Children's Books.

Rising Stars is grateful to the following people and schools who contributed to the development of these materials:
Plumcroft Primary School, London; St Helens Teaching Schools Alliance; St Nicholas CE Primary School, Chislehurst; St Margaret's CE Primary School, Heywood, Rochdale; Tennyson Road Primary School, Luton

All rights reserved. No part of this publication may be reproduced, stored in a retrieval system, or transmitted, in any form by any means, electronic, mechanical, photocopying, recording or otherwise, without the prior permission of Rising Stars.

British Library Cataloguing in Publication Data.
A CIP record for this book is available from the British Library.
ISBN: 978 1 78339 101 1

Printed by Ashford Colour Press

Contents

Introduction

Why use Rising Stars Assessment Progress Tests?

The *Rising Stars Assessment Reading Progress Tests* have been developed to support teachers assess the progress their pupils are making against the reading and comprehension requirements of the 2014 National Curriculum Programme of Study for English in Years 2 to 6. Separate progress tests are available to cover the requirements for grammar, punctuation, spelling and vocabulary. For Year 1 there is a single set of progress tests for English. These include reading, spelling, and grammar, punctuation and vocabulary tests. All *Rising Stars Assessment Progress Tests* are designed to support effective classroom assessment and are easy to use and mark.

The *Rising Stars Assessment Reading Progress Tests* include one test for each half term. All the tests have been:

- written by primary English assessment specialists
- reviewed by primary English curriculum and assessment experts.

How do the tests track progress?

The results data from the tests can be used to track progress. They show whether pupils are making the expected progress for their year, more than expected progress or less than expected progress. This data can then be used alongside other evidence to enable effective planning of future teaching and learning, for reporting to parents and as evidence for Ofsted inspections. If teachers are using the CD-ROM version of the tests, the results data can be keyed into the Progress Tracker (see pages 6–7 for more information) which automatically shows the progress of individual pupils against the Programme of Study and the results for all pupils by question and test. Data can also be exported into the school's management information system (MIS).

About the Reading Progress Tests

The tests are written to cover the requirements of the Programme of Study for the 2014 National Curriculum including the Appendices for English. There is a separate test for each half term. The number of marks for each test is as follows:

Year 2	Year 3	Year 4	Year 5	Year 6
15	20	20	20	20

The style of the tests mirrors that of the tests pupils will take at the end of Key Stage 2. Each test has two extracts with questions. The extracts used in the tests are authentic, age-appropriate ones and include fiction, poetry and non-fiction including those by well-known children's authors. Where possible the texts have been chosen to link to other subjects in the National Curriculum, in particular geography, history and science. The tests assess across a range of skills as exemplified by the assessment focuses for reading. The assessment focuses covered are:

AF2: understand, describe, select or retrieve information, events or ideas from texts and use quotation and reference to text;

AF3: deduce, infer or interpret information, events or ideas from texts;

AF4: identify and comment on the structure and organisation of texts, including grammatical and presentational features at text level;

AF5: explain and comment on writers' uses of language, including grammatical and literary features at word and sentence level;

AF6: identify and comment on writers' purposes and viewpoints and the overall effect of the text on the reader;

AF7: relate texts to their social, cultural and historical contexts and literary traditions.

Test demand

Test demand increases both within tests and across the year, which means that tests at the beginning of the year are easier than those at the end of the year. Within each test the Part A extract and questions is easier than the Part B extract and questions. As the year progresses the extracts and questions become increasingly more difficult.

Tracking progress

The marks pupils score in the tests can be used to track how they are progressing against the expected outcomes for their year group. The marks for each test have been split into three progress zones:

- less than expected progress
- expected progress
- more than expected progress.

The zones for each year group are as follows:

	Zone mark range		
	Less than expected progress	**Expected progress**	**More than expected progress**
Year 2	0–7	8–12	13–15
Year 3	0–10	11–16	17–20
Year 4	0–10	11–16	17–20
Year 5	0–10	11–16	17–20
Year 6	0–10	11–16	17–20

The table gives the mark ranges for the progress zones for each test which you can use to see how well each pupil is doing in each test. If pupils are making the expected progress for their year they will be consistently scoring marks in the middle zone of marks in the tests. The higher the mark in the zone, the more secure you can be that they are making expected progress.

How to use the Reading Progress Tests

Preparation and timings

1 Make enough copies of the test(s) for each pupil to have their own copy.
2 Hand out the papers and ensure pupils are seated appropriately so that they can't see each other's papers.
3 Pupils will need pens or pencils and erasers. Encourage pupils to cross out answers rather than rub them out.
4 There are no time limits for the tests but normal practice is to allow a minute per mark for written tests. Help with reading may be given using the same rules as when providing a reader with the DfE KS2 tests.

Supporting pupils during the tests

Before the test explain to the pupils that the test is an opportunity to show what they know, understand and can do. They should try to answer all the questions but should not worry if there are some they can't do.

Many pupils will be able to work independently in the tests, with minimal support from the teacher or a teaching assistant. However, pupils should be encouraged to 'have a go' at a question, or to move on to a fresh question if they appear to be stuck, to ensure that no pupil becomes distressed.

It is important that pupils receive appropriate support, but are not unfairly advantaged or disadvantaged. Throughout the tests, therefore, the teacher may read, explain or sign to a pupil any parts of the test that include instructions, for example by demonstrating how to circle an answer.

With younger age groups you may also consider using the version of the test on the CD-ROM and projecting it onto a whiteboard to support a whole class or group to take the tests. You may choose to refer to the words on the whiteboard and read them aloud so that pupils can follow them on the screen and on their own test paper and then write their answers on their papers individually.

Marking the tests

Use the detailed mark scheme and your professional judgement to award marks. Do not award half marks.

It is useful to use peer marking of test questions from time to time. Pupils should exchange test sheets and mark them as you read out the question and answer. You will need to check that pupils are marking accurately. This approach also provides an opportunity to recap on any questions that pupils found difficult to answer.

Feeding back to pupils

Once the test has been marked, use a five-minute feedback session with the pupils to help them review their answers. Wherever possible pupils should be encouraged to make their own corrections as in this way they will become more aware of their own strengths and weaknesses. Agree with each pupil what they did well in the test and what the targets are for them to improve. A template Pupil progress sheet is provided on page 8 for this purpose.

Using the Progress Tracker

The table on page 5 gives the mark ranges for the progress zones for each test which you can use to see how well each pupil is doing in each test. If pupils are making the expected progress for their year they will be consistently scoring marks in the middle zone of marks in the tests. The higher the mark in the zone, the more secure you can be that they are making expected progress.

The CD-ROM* version of *Reading Progress Tests* includes an interactive Progress Tracker, which allows you to enter the marks for each question for each test by pupil. This then automatically shows you which zone the pupil is in and also the zone distribution for the class so that you can track the progress of individual pupils and the whole class.

*If you have the book version only of *Reading Progress Tests*, the Progress Tracker can be downloaded from bit.ly/progtracker

The Progress Tracker also enables you to review the marks for each question so that you can identify areas where some or all pupils may need further support and areas where some or all pupils are ready to be stretched further.

If required, data from the tests can be exported into the school's management information system (MIS) so that it can be used alongside other data in whole school monitoring including the monitoring of specific groups of pupils, such as Pupil Premium.

Full details about the Progress Tracker are provided on the CD-ROM.

Pupil progress sheet

Name: _____ Class: _____ Date: _____

Test name: _____ Test number: _____ My mark: _____

What I did well in the test:

_____

_____

_____

What I need to do to improve:

1. _____

2. _____

3. _____

- -

Pupil progress sheet

Name: _____ Class: _____ Date: _____

Test name: _____ Test number: _____ My mark: _____

What I did well in the test:

_____

_____

_____

What I need to do to improve:

1. _____

2. _____

3. _____

8

© Rising Stars UK Ltd 2014   *You may photocopy this page*

This text is from *Tales of King Arthur*, retold by Felicity Brooks in the Usborne Classics Retold series.

The Sword in the Stone

'Please can I come with you?' begged Arthur. 'Please?'

He was watching his father and brother as they saddled their horses. They were about to go to a tournament, and Arthur was determined not to be left out. It had to be worth just one more try.

'I promise I won't get in the way, and I'll sharpen your weapons and shine up your armour and look after the horses,' he said, trying a direct appeal to his father. Sir Ector, who was busy loading the saddlebags, did not look up.

'You can't go,' said Kay dismissively. 'You're not even a knight.'

Kay, or rather Sir Kay, as Arthur now had to call him, had just been knighted, and he took great delight in reminding his brother of this fact. Now, after years of training, he was at last allowed to take part in a real tournament. His sword was razor-sharp, his brand-new armour had been polished to perfection, and he could hardly wait to show off his jousting skills. The last thing he wanted was his little brother tagging along behind him.

'But you'll need a **squire**,' said Arthur. 'Please let me be your squire.'

Sir Ector glanced down at Arthur's earnest, expectant face. There were good reasons why he didn't want him to go. He wished he could explain. But then, what harm could it really do?

'Well, Arthur, I suppose you might be useful…'

'But father!' protested Kay. Ector ignored him.

'And you'll be a knight yourself soon, so this will be a chance for you to learn how to behave. But one hint of trouble…'

'You won't even know I'm there,' grinned Arthur. He was already packing his bag. Kay shot him a filthy look and was still muttering under his breath when they set off.

The tournament had been arranged for New Year's Day, and people were coming

Glossary

squire – a boy or young man who served a knight and looked after his armour and weapons; squires were often knights in training.

© Rising Stars UK Ltd 2014   *You may photocopy this page*

from far and wide to take part or watch. Knights with their squires, dukes and earls, ladies on horseback, barons with their servants, whole families of peasants, wandering minstrels, shepherds, beggars, butchers, bakers, candlestickmakers and hordes of other curious onlookers thronged the muddy road, all heading for the town where the tournament was to take place. Ector soon realized that they'd have little chance of finding a place to stay unless one of them went ahead.

'I'll go,' said Arthur. 'I'll try the Blue Boar Inn first, and if there's no room there, I'll leave a message to say where I've gone.'

'All right,' said Ector. 'We'll meet you there. Ride safely!'

Arthur charged off at full gallop.

As soon as he was out of earshot, Ector turned to Kay conspiratorially.

'I think you should know that this isn't just any old tournament,' he said.

'What do you mean?' asked Kay.

'Well, the story I've heard is that the Archbishop has arranged it for a particular purpose.'

'And what's that?'

'To find the new king,' said Ector.

© Rising Stars UK Ltd 2014   *You may photocopy this page*

This poem is by Gillian Clarke.

The Titanic

Under the ocean where water falls
over the decks and tilted walls
where the sea comes knocking at the great ship's door,
the band still plays
to the drum of the waves,
to the drum of the waves.

Down in the indigo depths of the sea
the white shark waltzes gracefully
down the water stairways, across the ballroom floor
where the cold shoals flow
and ghost dancers go,
ghost dancers go.

Their dresses are frayed, their shoes are lost.
their jewels and beads and bones are tossed
into the sand, all turned to stone,
as they sing in the sea
eternally,
eternally.

Currents comb their long loose hair,
dancers sway forever where
the bright fish nibble their glittering bones,
till they fall asleep
in the shivering deep,
in the shivering deep.

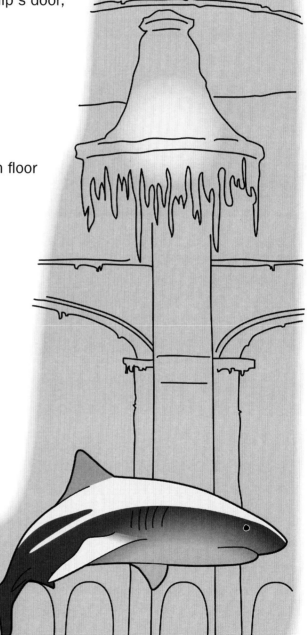

Name:	Class:	Date:

The Sword in the Stone

1 From what you learn in the passage, tick to show whether the following are **fact** or **opinion**.

	Fact	Opinion
Kay has just been knighted.		
Kay thinks that Arthur is annoying.		
Kay is older than Arthur.		

AF2

1 mark

2 *'And you'll be a knight yourself soon, so this will be a chance for you to learn how to behave. But one hint of trouble...'*

What does *But one hint of trouble…* mean? Tick **one**.

Someone has hinted that Arthur might cause trouble. ☐

Arthur will be sent home if he misbehaves. ☐

Arthur might find the tournament difficult. ☐

Ector thinks Arthur will be badly behaved. ☐

AF3

1 mark

3 Why is Kay muttering under his breath when they set off for the tournament? Explain your answer fully, using the text to help you.

_____

_____

AF3

2 marks

/ 4

Total for this page

© Rising Stars UK Ltd 2014   *You may photocopy this page*

4 Number these events to show the order in which they happen.
The first one has been done for you.

☐ Arthur rides ahead to the Blue Boar Inn.

☐ Kay tells Arthur he can't go.

☐ Ector explains the purpose of the tournament.

☐ Ector agrees to let Arthur go.

1 Arthur pleads with his father to let him go to the tournament.

AF4

1 mark

---

5 *Arthur charged off at full gallop.*
As soon as he was out of earshot, Ector turned to Kay conspiratorially.

What impression does the phrase *Ector turned to Kay conspiratorially* give
of Ector? Tick **one**.

He is a criminal. ☐

He favours Kay over Arthur. ☐

He is friendly. ☐

He wants to tell Kay something he doesn't want Arthur to hear. ☐

AF5

1 mark

---

6 Look at the paragraph beginning: *The tournament…*
What is this paragraph **mainly** about? Tick **two**.

The tournament is being held in a town. ☐

It is a winter tournament. ☐

A lot of people are going to the tournament. ☐

The road into the town is muddy. ☐

It may be difficult to find a place to stay. ☐

AF6

1 mark

/ 3

Total for this page

© Rising Stars UK Ltd 2014   *You may photocopy this page*

7 One of the aspects of Arthur's character is his strong will.
What evidence is there in the passage to support this opinion?
Explain as fully as you can, using the text to help you answer.

_____

_____

_____

AF6

2 marks

---

8 Which of the following descriptions best fits this passage? Tick **one**.

a legend ☐

an historical account ☐

a fairy tale ☐

a fable ☐

AF7

1 mark

/ 10

Total for this test

© Rising Stars UK Ltd 2014   *You may photocopy this page*

Name:	Class:	Date:

The Titanic

1 Write **one** word from the whole poem in each space below to complete the pairs of rhyming words. One has been done for you.

falls	walls
sea	
flow	
hair	

AF4
1 mark

---

2 Look at these lines from the first verse:

over the decks and tilted walls
where the sea comes knocking at the great ship's door,
the band still plays

In **your own words**, what do these lines tell you about the *Titanic*?
Write **two** things.

1 _____

2 _____

AF3
2 marks

---

3 Look at these lines from the first verse:

the band still plays
to the drum of the waves,

What do these lines suggest about the waves?

_____

AF3
1 mark

/ 4
Total for this page

© Rising Stars UK Ltd 2014 *You may photocopy this page*

4 Why does the poet say that *the white shark waltzes*?

_____

_____

AF5

1 mark

---

5 Look at this line from the last verse:

the bright fish nibble their glittering bones,

Think about the phrase *glittering bones*. Which of the following could replace it in the poem while keeping the same meaning? Tick **one**.

shiny stones ☐

skeletons clean ☐

sparkling jewels ☐

colourful fish ☐

AF2

1 mark

---

6 This poem uses alliteration (repeated sounds).
For example:

as they s̲ing in the s̲ea

Find and copy **one** other line from the poem that uses alliteration.
Underline the repeated sounds.

_____

AF5

1 mark

/ 3

Total for this page

© Rising Stars UK Ltd 2014   *You may photocopy this page*

7 Draw lines to match each phrase with what it shows you about the dancers.

Phrase	The dancers...
their jewels and beads	have been there a long time
all turned to stone	don't look as good as they once did
and ghost dancers go	are wealthy
Their dresses are frayed, their shoes are lost	are dead

AF5
1 mark

---

8 The poem is very rhythmical (has a strong rhythm). Why do you think the poet chose to make the poem so rhythmical?

_____

_____

AF6
1 mark

---

9 Think about the whole poem. What is it **mainly** about?
Tick the **best** answer.

music ☐

the ocean ☐

dancing ☐

death ☐

AF6
1 mark

/ 10
Total for this test

© Rising Stars UK Ltd 2014   *You may photocopy this page*

This text is from *The Firework-Maker's Daughter* by Philip Pullman, adapted for the stage by Stephen Russell.

The Firework-Maker's Daughter

ACT 1

1 – LALCHAND'S WORKSHOP

Workbenches, chemicals, rockets, etc. A fuse is laid leading to a firework. A scruffy and dirty girl, LILA, comes onstage. She carefully adds a tiny amount of delicate powder to the firework, thinks about it, adds a tiny bit more. She thinks 'why not' and pours a load in. She steps back and lights the fuse. It burns quickly towards the firework. LILA takes cover offstage.

A man, LALCHAND the Firework-Maker, walks into the workshop. He watches the fuse for a moment, then stands on it, putting it out.

LALCHAND: Lila!

LILA returns.

LALCHAND: What's this?

LILA: A rudimentary experiment, father.

LALCHAND grunts.

LILA: A standard Java Light, with cloud powder instead of flowers of salt.

LALCHAND: (*Impressed.*) Have you given it a name?

LILA: Tumbling Demons.

LALCHAND: Excellent. If it works I'll put it in the New Year Festival display.

LILA: That's three of my fireworks in your display.

LALCHAND: I know, and I'll let everybody else know too, *if* I win.

LILA: *When* you win.

LALCHAND: From your mouth to the King's ears, eh?

LILA throws some matches to LALCHAND. LALCHAND strikes a match.

LILA: There's a poster in the market. They've announced the other competitors.

LALCHAND's interested and forgets about the lit match.

LALCHAND: Who do I have to beat this year?

© Rising Stars UK Ltd 2014   *You may photocopy this page*

LILA: The usual lot. The greatest firework-makers in the world.

LALCHAND: Who are the favourites?

LILA: Herr Puffenflasch, of course.

LALCHAND: The King likes him. Ouch!

The match burns LALCHAND's fingers.

LILA: The King loves him, but he can't win three years in a row.

LALCHAND lights another match, sets it to the fuse and steps back.

LILA: And there's an American – Colonel Sam Sparkington. No one knows anything about him.

LALCHAND: You know what the Americans are like, they never go anywhere unless they're sure they're going to win.

(Talking about the firework.)

               Did you put anything else in this?

LILA: A little scorpion oil.

LALCHAND: One drop or two?

LILA: A teaspoon.

LALCHAND: (*Horrified.*) A teaspoon!?

The firework explodes. LALCHAND and LILA have all but had the clothes blown off them.

LILA: That's too much, isn't it.

LALCHAND: You could've blown up the whole city! You don't know enough to use those ingredients.

LILA: If you made me your apprentice I'd learn about things like that.

LALCHAND: So it's my fault you nearly killed us, is it? You're such an ignorant girl!

LILA: I know about most things.

LALCHAND: What are the ingredients of fly-away powder?

LALCHAND waves his hand and creates a shower of sparks in the air.

LILA: I don't know that.

LALCHAND: Where do you find thunder-grains?

LALCHAND throws a thunder-grain at LILA's feet. It makes a loud bang. LILA jumps.

LILA: Or that.

LALCHAND: There's no limit to the things you don't know.

LILA: I know about the secret!

LALCHAND: What?

LILA: I know about the secret. The secret all firework-makers have to know.

LALCHAND: What is it?

N.B: Remember that you should never play with fireworks. It is extremely dangerous.

This text is adapted from: www.ducksters.com

Michelangelo

 Growing up

Michelangelo Buonarotti was born in Caprese, Italy on March 6, 1475. He was still young when his family moved to Florence where Michelangelo grew up. His mother died when he was only six years old.

Growing up in Florence during the Italian Renaissance was the perfect environment for young Michelangelo. Even as a child all he wanted to do was paint and be an artist. His father, a local government official, wanted Michelangelo to go to school, but he had little interest in school. At the age of thirteen he was apprenticed to Domenico Ghirlandaio, a painter and artist.

 Training to be an artist

Michelangelo's talents became apparent as he worked for Ghirlandaio. Within a year or so he was sent to the powerful Medici family to continue his training under the sculptor Bertoldo di Geovanni. Michelangelo was able to work with some of the finest artists and philosophers of the time.

 The Pieta

In 1496 Michelangelo moved to Rome. A year later he received a commission to make a sculpture called the Pieta. It would become one of the masterpieces of Renaissance art. The sculpture shows Jesus after he was crucified lying on the lap of his mother Mary. Today this sculpture sits in St. Peter's Basilica in the Vatican. It is the only piece of art that Michelangelo signed.

 Statue of David

Michelangelo's fame as a great artist began to grow. He returned to Florence and received another commission to create a large statue of David the giant-killer. It took him a couple of years to finish the enormous statue. The piece of marble he began with was very tall and thin. Many people didn't think he could do much with it. He worked in secrecy, not letting anyone see it until it was finished.

David became Michelangelo's most famous work of art. It is thirteen feet tall and was the largest statue made since Ancient Roman times. It is considered by many experts in art to be a near perfect sculpture. Today the statue resides at the Academy of Fine Arts in Florence, Italy.

© Rising Stars UK Ltd 2014   *You may photocopy this page*

Sistine Chapel

In 1505 Michelangelo returned to Rome. He was commissioned by the Pope in 1508 to paint the ceiling of the Sistine Chapel. Michelangelo considered himself to be a sculptor, but agreed to paint the Sistine Chapel for the Pope. He worked for four years, painting upside down on a scaffold in order to finish the painting. The painting was huge (141 feet long by 43 feet wide). It contained nine scenes from the Bible down its centre. The most famous of all the scenes is The Creation of Adam. At the centre of the scene, God's hand and Adam's hand nearly touch. This is one of the most recreated scenes in all of art and, along with the Mona Lisa, is one of the most famous paintings in history.

Interesting facts about Michelangelo

- His full name was Michelangelo di Lodovico Buonarroti Simoni.

- When he was seventeen he was hit on the nose by fellow artist Pietro Torrigiano in an argument. His nose was severely broken as can be seen in the portraits we have of Michelangelo.

- He painted The Last Judgment, a famous painting on the wall of the Sistine Chapel.

- He was also a poet who wrote over 300 poems.

© Rising Stars UK Ltd 2014 *You may photocopy this page*

Name:	Class:	Date:

The Firework-Maker's Daughter

1 Where is this scene set?

_____

AF2
1 mark

---

2 Which of the following is true about Lalchand? Tick **one**.

He wants to win the New Year Festival display. ☐

He is confident he will win the New Year Festival display. ☐

He spoils Lila. ☐

He is keen to make Lila his apprentice. ☐

AF2
1 mark

---

3 Read these lines from the text:

LALCHAND: I know, and I'll let everybody else know too, *if* I win.
LILA: *When* you win.

Why does Lila say _When_ you win?

_____

AF3
1 mark

/ 3
Total for this page

© Rising Stars UK Ltd 2014   *You may photocopy this page*

4 Draw lines to match each aspect of the text with how it is shown.
One has been done for you.

Aspect of text	How it is shown
stage directions	capital letters
direct speech	italics
characters' names	underlined capital letters
scene titles	standard text

AF4
1 mark

---

5 Read these lines from the text:

LILA: The usual lot. The greatest firework-makers in the world.
LALCHAND: Who are the favourites?
LILA: Herr Puffenflasch, of course.

Why has the writer chosen to use the name *Herr Puffenflasch*?

_____

AF5
1 mark

---

6 Number these events to show the order in which they happen.
The first one has been done for you.

☐ A firework goes off.

1 Lila lights a firework.

☐ Lalchand burns his fingers.

☐ Lalchand asks Lila questions to test her knowledge.

☐ Lila tells Lalchand about the poster in the market place.

AF4
1 mark

/ 3
Total for this page

© Rising Stars UK Ltd 2014   *You may photocopy this page*

7 In this scene what mood is the writer aiming to create in the audience?
Tick the **best** answer.

relaxation ☐

tension ☐

fear ☐

amusement ☐

AF6

1 mark

---

8 Look at the first part of the dialogue, from *LALCHAND: Lila!* to *LILA: Tumbling Demons*. **Find** and **copy a phrase** that means the same as 'a simple test'.

_____

AF2

1 mark

---

9 Lalchand says to Lila: *You're such an ignorant girl!*
Explain whether you think this is true, giving **two** reasons to support your answer.

_____

_____

_____

AF3

2 marks

/ 10

Total for this test

© Rising Stars UK Ltd 2014   *You may photocopy this page*

Name:	Class:	Date:

Michelangelo

1   Which of the following descriptions best fits this text? Tick **one**.

autobiography ☐   biography ☐

account ☐   report ☐

AF7   1 mark

---

2   Michelangelo was a sculptor. According to the text, **what else** was he? Tick **two**.

a philosopher ☐   a government official ☐

a painter ☐   a poet ☐

a scientist ☐

AF2   1 mark

---

3   Look at the section headed *Statue of David*. **Find** and **copy a sentence** to show that Michelangelo did a good job of sculpting a statue of David.

_____

_____

AF2   1 mark

---

4   Tick to show whether the following sentences about Michelangelo are **true** or **false**. The first one has been done for you.

	True	False
He was born in Florence.		✓
He enjoyed his time at school.		
He could be argumentative.		
Painting was the art form he loved the most.		
He was not happy with the Pieta.		

AF3   2 marks

/ 5   Total for this page

© Rising Stars UK Ltd 2014   *You may photocopy this page*

5 Look at the section headed *Sistine Chapel.*
What is the main point the writer is trying to make about Michelangelo?
Tick **one**.

He was a sculptor. ☐

He was religious. ☐

He was famous. ☐

He was dedicated. ☐

AF6

1 mark

6 Michelangelo was a very talented artist.
How do you know this? Explain as fully as you can, using the text to help you.

_____

_____

_____

_____

AF3

2 marks

7 Draw lines to match each phrase with what it shows you about
Michelangelo.

Phrase

all he wanted to do was...
be an artist

He... wrote over 300 poems

the only piece of art that
Michelangelo signed

he was hit on the nose...
in an argument

one of the masterpieces of
Renaissance art

Michelangelo was...

uninterested in fame

exceptionally talented

single-minded

hot-headed

creative

AF5

2 marks

/ 10

Total for this test

© Rising Stars UK Ltd 2014 *You may photocopy this page*

This text is adapted from *The Usborne History of Britain* by Ruth Brocklehurst.

Prehistoric Britain

The story of life in Britain goes back to a time before people knew how to read and write, in an era known as prehistory. Although Britain's earliest inhabitants didn't write anything down, they did leave other clues behind. Traces of their houses, their tools and ornaments, and sometimes even their bodies, have survived down the ages. They help to build up a picture of how people lived in Britain from around 700,000 years ago.

The Ice Age

When early people first set foot in Britain, things were very different from today. It was a period when temperatures swung between extremes. For thousands of years at a time it was bitterly cold. The sea that now divides Britain from the continent of Europe wasn't there, as much of the water was frozen into ice. Rivers of ice criss-crossed the land, and people, animals and plants just couldn't survive.

But, every hundred thousand years or so, the weather grew warmer and the ice melted. Plants grew, attracting herds of animals, such as mammoths, deer and wild horses, cattle and pigs. They walked to Britain on the dry land that connected it to Europe.

Hunting and gathering

The first people arrived in Britain on foot, following the animals. They needed animals to survive – they ate their meat and used their skins for clothes. But many animals were huge and fierce, and people only had simple hunting tools, such as pointed wooden spears. So they chased animals for long distances to tire them out, or scared them off cliffs or into bogs (areas of wet, spongy ground), to make killing them easier.

They also made use of any animals they found that were already dead. This saved the effort of hunting. But the hunters of the Ice Age didn't just eat meat. They also caught fish and gathered shellfish, wild nuts, fruits and roots. They twisted plant stems and leaves to make rope and twine. And, to help with all these tasks, they made themselves tools from wood, bone and stone.

On the move

Because they relied so much on wild animals, Ice Age hunters didn't have fixed homes. They moved around, following herds as they migrated in search of the best grass. At night, people slept in caves – if any were handy – or in shelters made of things they found nearby. But, every hundred thousand years or so, the cold weather returned again, the ice expanded to cover more of the land, and people and animals had to leave once more.

Getting warmer

During the Ice Age, the weather kept swinging from very cold to warm – though this happened very slowly, about every 100,000 years. Plants, animals and people could only survive in Britain in the warm periods.

In 2003, archaeologists discovered rare Ice Age art in caves at Creswell Crags in Nottinghamshire. Outlines of deer, wild cattle and bird-like creatures survive, carved into the cave walls.

© Rising Stars UK Ltd 2014   *You may photocopy this page*

This text is from *Carrie's War* by Nina Bawden, adapted for the stage by Emma Reeves.

Carrie's War

ACT 1
DRUID'S GROVE

Darkness. The wind whistles through the trees in the grove. Train sound effects. Smoke, as if from a train. Loud train whistle – an unearthly shriek, 'more like a volcano erupting than a steam engine blowing its top'. Mixed in with the whistling sound is a girl's scream. The sound dies away.

Sounds of a summer's day. Daytime, in a wooded, shady place where the light has had to make its way through layers of foliage. Near the top of the slope, ADULT CARRIE pushes through the trees, and enters with a suitcase. She is breathless, as if she has just run up a hill. She is wearing a long, flowing coat. She pauses on the brink and gazes downwards. The unearthly whistle, not as loud as before – as if in CARRIE's memory. CARRIE shudders, and sways on the brink of the slope. The sound dies away.

CARRIE'S SON enters through the trees, brushing off bits of leaf and twig. He is wearing jeans, etc. – 1970s clothes with a strong contemporary feel.

....

SON: Mum?

CARRIE turns and looks at him blankly.

                Mum! How much further?

CARRIE: No further. That's it.

CARRIE points off into the distance, down the slope. Her son looks.

SON: That old ruin?

CARRIE: I forgot – I've been away a long time.

CARRIE wanders down the slope. Her SON sits down on his mum's suitcase, and munches on a chocolate bar.

SON:	Looks like no one's been here for hundreds of years.
CARRIE:	No. No – it's only – (*With wonder.*) thirty years...
SON:	Exactly.
CARRIE:	We used to come here all the time, during the war. Me, and little Nick.
SON:	Little Nick? What, fat Uncle Nick?
CARRIE:	He wasn't fat then. Actually, he looked a lot like you.

CARRIE'S SON offers his chocolate bar to his mum.

SON:	D'you want the rest of this?

CARRIE shakes her head. She walks along the top of the bank.

CARRIE:	Nick and I used to walk here from the town, along the side of the railway.
SON:	What railway?
CARRIE:	There used to be a railway. This is the exact spot where the train whistled when it came round the bend. Right by the slope down to Druid's Bottom.
SON:	Druid's Bottom?
CARRIE:	(*Laughs.*) That's the name of the house. Druid's Bottom. Because it's at the bottom of Druid's Grove.
SON:	What's Druid's Grove?
CARRIE:	This is. Thousands of years ago, this place was sacred to the Druids. The Old Religion. There's a spring that's supposed to have healing powers, and a stone circle – the remains of a temple. Well, it might be. Albert thought it went back to the Iron Age.
SON:	Who's Albert?
CARRIE:	Albert Sandwich. He thought there might have been an Iron Age settlement here. He was interested in that sort of thing.
SON:	Dad would have been.
CARRIE:	Yes. Dad would have been interested, too. Albert and your dad were quite alike. In some ways.

Pause. The stage darkens as the sun passes behind a cloud. A faint, rumbling noise of ancient breathing.

CARRIE:	Listen.
SON:	What for?
CARRIE:	Something old, and huge – and nameless.
SON:	(*Unimpressed.*) You mean like a ghost? A monster?
CARRIE:	Nothing so simple. Albert said the druids used to make human sacrifices...
SON:	You're being weird, you do know that, don't you?

© Rising Stars UK Ltd 2014 *You may photocopy this page*

Name:	Class:	Date:

Prehistoric Britain

1 When did people first arrive in Britain?

_____

AF2

1 mark

2 Draw lines to match the objects used by the earliest inhabitants of Britain to the materials they used to make them. One has been done for you.

Objects	Materials
spears	plant stems and leaves
rope	animal skins
tools	things found nearby
clothes	wood
shelters	wood, bone and stone

AF2

1 mark

3 Tick to show whether the following sentences about the first inhabitants of Britain are **true** or **false**. The first one has been done for you.

	True	False
They could not read or write.	✓	
They relied heavily on the tools they made.		
They built permanent settlements.		
They stayed in Britain throughout the Ice Age.		
They used clever hunting techniques.		

AF3

2 marks

/ 4

Total for this page

4   Why would chasing a large animal into a bog make it easier to kill?

_____

AF3

1 mark

---

5   Look at the paragraph headed *On the move.*
What do you find out about Ice Age people? Write **two** things.

1 _____

2 _____

AF2

2 marks

---

6   Which of the following descriptions best fits this text? Tick **one**.

explanation   ☐

persuasion   ☐

recount   ☐

report   ☐

AF7

1 mark

/ 4

Total for this page

© Rising Stars UK Ltd 2014   *You may photocopy this page*

7 Think about the whole text. What is it **mainly** about? Tick the **best** answer.

The people who lived in Britain during the Ice Age ☐

The weather in Britain during the Ice Age ☐

The animals in Britain during the Ice Age ☐

The geography of Britain during the Ice Age ☐

AF6
1 mark

8 Where would you expect to find this text? Tick the **best** answer.

in a newsletter ☐

in a textbook ☐

in a catalogue ☐

in a magazine ☐

AF7
1 mark

/ 10
Total for this test

Name:	Class:	Date:

Carrie's War

1   Draw lines to match each word with its meaning in the text.
One has been done for you.

Word	**Meaning**
unearthly	belonging to the present day
brink	priest of an ancient religion
contemporary	strange or supernatural
sacred	edge of a steep place
druid	holy

AF2

1 mark

---

2   Read these lines from the text:

SON: Mum?

CARRIE turns and looks at him blankly.

Why does Carrie look at her son blankly? Tick the **best** answer.

She is annoyed with him.   ☐

She doesn't recognise him.   ☐

She doesn't hear him call her.   ☐

She is preoccupied by her thoughts. ☐

AF3

1 mark

---

3   Look at this line from the text.

CARRIE: No. No – it's only – (*With wonder.*) thirty years...

What does *With wonder* tell you here?

_____

AF2

1 mark

/ 3

Total for this page

© Rising Stars UK Ltd 2014   *You may photocopy this page*

4 Why does Carrie's son offer his chocolate bar to his mum?

_____

AF3

1 mark

---

5 Stage directions are written in italics.

At a later stage, the directions are indented and look different to the beginning of the play script.

SON: D'you want the rest of this?

CARRIE shakes her head. She walks along the top of the bank.

Why do you think the writer has indented the later stage directions?

_____

AF4

1 mark

---

6 Look at these sentences that the writer uses in the text.

Dad would have been.
Yes, Dad would have been interested, too.
Albert and your dad were quite alike.

Why has the writer included these sentences?

_____

_____

AF5

1 mark

AF3

/ 3

Total for this page

© Rising Stars UK Ltd 2014   *You may photocopy this page*

7 Read these lines from the text.

CARRIE points off into the distance, down the slope. Her son looks.

SON: That old ruin?

CARRIE: I forgot – I've been away a long time.

CARRIE wanders down the slope. Her SON sits down on his mum's suitcase, and munches on a chocolate bar.

SON: Looks like no one's been here for hundreds of years.

CARRIE: No. No – it's only – (*With wonder.*) thirty years...

SON: Exactly.

From what Carrie's son says here, what can you tell about his attitude towards the house? Tick **one**.

He is wary of it.   ☐

He is curious about it.   ☐

He is excited by it.   ☐

He is unimpressed by it.   ☐

AF5
1 mark

---

8 a) How does the writer create an eerie atmosphere in this scene?
Write **two** things.

_____

_____

_____

AF6
2 marks

b) The writer lightens the eeriness with humour. How does she do this?
Mention **one** thing.

_____

AF6
1 mark

/ 10
Total for this test

© Rising Stars UK Ltd 2014   *You may photocopy this page*

This text is from *Stig of the Dump* by Clive King.

Barney and the Chalk Pit

If you went too near the edge of the chalk pit the ground would give way. Barney had been told this often enough. Everybody had told him. His grandmother, every time he came to stay with her. His sister, every time she wasn't telling him something else. Barney had a feeling, somewhere in his middle, that it was probably true about the ground giving way. But still, there was a difference between being told and seeing it happen. And today was one of those grey days when there was nothing to do, nothing to play, and nowhere to go. Except the chalk pit. The dump.

Barney got through the rickety fence and went to the edge of the pit. This had been the side of a hill once, he told himself. Men had come to dig away chalk and left this huge hole in the earth. He thought of all the sticks of chalk they must have made, and all the blackboards in all the schools they must have written on. They must have dug and dug for hundreds of years. And then they got tired of digging, or somebody had told them to stop before they dug away all the hill. And now they did not know what to do with this empty hole and they were trying to fill it up again. Anything people didn't want they threw into the bottom of the pit.

He crawled through the rough grass and peered over. The sides of the pit were white chalk, with lines of flints poking out like bones in places. At the top was crumbly brown earth and the roots of the trees that grew on the edge. The roots looped over the edge, twined in the air and grew back into the earth. Some of the trees hung over the edge, holding on desperately by a few roots. The earth and chalk had fallen away beneath them, and one day they too would fall to the bottom of the pit. Strings of ivy and the creeper called Old Man's Beard hung in the air.

Far below was the bottom of the pit. The dump. Barney could see strange bits of wreckage among the moss and elder bushes and nettles. Was that the steering wheel of a ship? The tail of an aeroplane? At least there was a real bicycle. Barney felt sure he could make it go if only he could get at it. They didn't let him have a bicycle.

Barney wished he was at the bottom of the pit.

And the ground gave way.

Barney felt his head going down and his feet going up. There was a rattle of falling earth beneath him. Then he was falling, still clutching the clump of grass that was falling with him.

This is what it's like when the ground gives way, thought Barney. Then he seemed to turn a complete somersault in the air, bumped into a ledge of chalk halfway down, crashed through some creepers and ivy and branches, and landed on a bank of moss.

His thoughts did those funny things they do when you bump your head and you suddenly find yourself thinking about what you had for dinner last Tuesday, all mixed up with seven times six. Barney lay with his eyes shut, waiting for his thoughts to stop being mixed up. Then he opened them.

© Rising Stars UK Ltd 2014   *You may photocopy this page*

This poem is by Benjamin Zephaniah.

Talking Turkeys

Be nice to yu turkeys dis christmas
Cos' turkeys just wanna hav fun
Turkeys are cool, turkeys are wicked
An every turkey has a Mum.
Be nice to yu turkeys dis christmas,
Don't eat it, keep it alive,
It could be yu mate, an not on your plate
Say, Yo! Turkey I'm on your side.
I got lots of friends who are turkeys
An all of dem fear christmas time,
Dey wanna enjoy it, dey say humans destroyed it
An humans are out of dere mind,
Yeah, I got lots of friends who are turkeys
Dey all hav a right to a life,
Not to be caged up an genetically made up
By any farmer an his wife.

Turkeys just wanna play reggae
Turkeys just wanna hip-hop
Can yu imagine a nice young turkey saying,
'I cannot wait for de chop',
Turkeys like getting presents, dey wanna watch christmas TV,
Turkeys hav brains an turkeys feel pain
In many ways like yu an me.

I once knew a turkey called…Turkey
He said 'Benji explain to me please,
Who put de turkey in christmas
An what happens to christmas trees?',
I said 'I am not too sure turkey
But it's nothing to do wid Christ Mass
Humans get greedy an waste more dan need be
An business men mek loadsa cash'.

Be nice to yu turkey dis christmas
Invite dem indoors fe sum greens
Let dem eat cake an let dem partake
In a plate of organic grown beans,
Be nice to yu turkey dis christmas
An spare dem de cut of de knife,
Join Turkeys United an dey'll be delighted
An yu will mek new friends 'FOR LIFE'.

© Rising Stars UK Ltd 2014   *You may photocopy this page*

Name:	Class:	Date:

Barney and the Chalk Pit

1 What is at the bottom of the chalk pit?

_____

AF2

1 mark

- -

2 Look at the first paragraph, beginning *If you went…*
Find and **copy a sentence** to show that Barney was bored.

_____

_____

AF2

1 mark

- -

3 Look at the second paragraph, beginning *Barney got through…*
What do you find out about the chalk pit? Write **two** things.

1 _____

2 _____

AF2

1 mark

- -

4 Look at the third paragraph, beginning *He crawled through…*
What point is the writer trying to make about the chalk pit? Tick **one**.

It is large.   ☐

Its edge is unstable. ☐

It is deep.   ☐

It is used as a dump. ☐

It was once a hill.   ☐

AF6

1 mark

/ 4

Total for this page

© Rising Stars UK Ltd 2014   *You may photocopy this page*

5 Look at the third paragraph, beginning *He crawled through…*
How does the writer create a sense of danger in this paragraph?
Give **two** examples.

1 _____

2 _____

AF5

2 marks

---

6 Number these events from 1 to 5 to show the order in which they happen.
One has been numbered for you.

☐   Barney crashes through creepers and ivy.

4   Barney lands on a bank of moss.

☐   Barney bumps into a ledge.

☐   Barney opens his eyes.

☐   Barney turns a somersault.

AF4

1 mark

---

7 *Barney wished he was at the bottom of the pit.*

Why did Barney wish he was at the bottom of the pit?

_____

_____

AF3

1 mark

/ 4

Total for this page

© Rising Stars UK Ltd 2014   *You may photocopy this page*

8 Look at this extract from the text.

Barney felt his head going down and his feet going up. There was a rattle of falling earth beneath him. Then he was falling, still clutching the clump of grass that was falling with him.
*   This is what it's like when the ground gives way, thought Barney.*

What does the last sentence of the extract suggest about Barney?

_____

_____

AF3

1 mark

---

9 Look at this extract from the text.

His thoughts did those funny things they do when you bump your head and you suddenly find yourself thinking about what you had for dinner last Tuesday, all mixed up with seven times six.

What does this mean? Tick **one**.

Barney found everything funny.   ☐

Barney was trying to think about more than one thing at a time. ☐

Barney's thinking was confused.   ☐

AF3

Barney was trying to remember his times tables.   ☐

1 mark

/ 10

Total for this test

Name:	Class:	Date:

Talking Turkeys

1 Some of the words in the poem are written using non-standard spelling.
Look at the words in the table. Write a word in each empty space to show how you would spell each word using standard spelling. One has been done for you.

Spelling from the poem	Standard spelling
dem	them
dey	
wid	
mek	
fe	

AF5
1 mark

---

2 Why is the poem written using non-standard spelling? Tick **one**.

The poet is imagining how turkeys might spell. ☐

The poet is experimenting with language. ☐

The poet doesn't know how to spell. ☐

The poet speaks in a dialect that is not Standard English. ☐

The poet wants to make the poem hard to read. ☐

AF5
1 mark

---

3 Look at the second verse, beginning *Turkeys just wanna play reggae…*
Find and **copy a line** from this verse that tells you that turkeys get killed.

AF2
1 mark

_____

/ 3
Total for this page

© Rising Stars UK Ltd 2014   *You may photocopy this page*

4 Write one word from the poem to complete the pairs of rhyming words.
Tick the box to show whether it is a full rhyme or a half rhyme.
The first two have been done for you.

Pair of rhyming words		Full rhyme	Half rhyme
fun	Mum		✓
life	wife	✓	
time			
please			
greens			

AF4
1 mark

5 Read these lines from the poem.

'But it's nothing to do with Christ Mass
Humans get greedy an waste more dan need be
An business men mek loadsa cash.'

What do these lines tell you about the poet? Tick the **best** answer.

The poet doesn't like greed. ☐

The poet doesn't like Christmas. ☐

The poet doesn't like money. ☐

The poet doesn't like businessmen. ☐

AF6
1 mark

6 In what way is the title of the poem a play on words?

_____

_____

AF2
1 mark

/ 3
Total for this page

© Rising Stars UK Ltd 2014   *You may photocopy this page*

7 Think about the whole poem. What point does the poet want to make?
Tick the **best** answer.

Turkeys fear Christmas. ☐

Turkeys have brains. ☐

Turkeys have a right to life. ☐

Turkeys are like us in many ways. ☐

Turkeys feel pain. ☐

AF6

1 mark

---

8 The poet says that turkeys are *like yu an me*.
Write **three ways**, according to the poet, in which turkeys are like humans.

1 _____

2 _____

3 _____

AF3

2 marks

---

9 How would you describe this poem? Tick **one**.

ballad ☐

limerick ☐

free verse ☐

rhyming verse ☐

AF7

1 mark

/ 10

Total for this test

© Rising Stars UK Ltd 2014   *You may photocopy this page*

This poem is by Brian Patten.

Geography Lesson

Our teacher told us one day he would leave
And sail across a warm blue sea
To places he had only known from maps,
And all his life had longed to be.

The house he lived in was narrow and grey
But in his mind's eye he could see
Sweet-scented jasmine clinging to the walls,
And green leaves burning on an orange tree.

He spoke of the lands he longed to visit,
Where it was never drab or cold.
I couldn't understand why he never left,
And shook off the school's stranglehold.

Then halfway through his final term
He took ill and never returned,
And he never got to that place on the map
Where the green leaves of the orange trees burned.

The maps were redrawn on the classroom wall;
His name was forgotten, it faded away.
But a lesson he never knew he taught
Is with me to this day.

I travel to where the green leaves burn
To where the ocean's glass-clear and blue,
To all those places my teacher taught me to love
But which he never knew.

This text is taken from *Five Children and It* by E. Nesbit.

The Creature in the Sand

Five children – Robert, Anthea, Jane, Cyril and the Baby – explore a gravel pit near their new home. When they dig a hole in the sand they are surprised to find a strange creature.

The children stood round the hole in a ring, looking at the creature they had found. It was worth looking at. Its eyes were on long horns like a snail's eyes, and it could move them in and out like telescopes; it had ears like a bat's ears, and its tubby body was shaped like a spider's and covered with thick soft fur; its legs and arms were furry too, and it had hands and feet like a monkey's.

'What on earth is it?' Jane said. 'Shall we take it home?'

The thing turned its long eyes to look at her and said –

'Does she always talk nonsense, or is it only the rubbish on her head that makes her silly?'

It looked scornfully at Jane's hat as it spoke.

'She doesn't mean to be silly,' Anthea said gently; 'we none of us do, whatever you may think! Don't be frightened; we don't want to hurt you, you know.'

'Hurt *me*!' it said. '*Me* frightened? Upon my word! Why, you talk as if I were nobody in particular.' All its fur stood out like a cat's when it is going to fight.

'Well,' said Anthea, still kindly, 'perhaps if we knew who you are in particular we could think of something to say that wouldn't make you angry. Everything we've said so far seems to have done so. Who are you? And don't get angry! Because really we don't know.'

© Rising Stars UK Ltd 2014   *You may photocopy this page*

'You don't know?' it said. 'Well, I knew the world had changed – but – well, really –Do you mean to tell me seriously you don't know a Psammead when you see one?'

'A Sammyadd? That's Greek to me.'

'So it is to everyone,' said the creature sharply. 'Well, in plain English, then, a *Sand-fairy*. Don't you know a Sand-fairy when you see one?'

It looked so grieved and hurt that Jane hastened to say, 'Of course I see you are, *now*. It's quite plain now one comes to look at you.'

'You came to look at me, several sentences ago,' it said crossly, beginning to curl up again in the sand.

'Oh – don't go away again! Do talk some more,' Robert cried. 'I didn't know you were a Sand-fairy, but I knew directly I saw you that you were much the wonderfullest thing I'd ever seen.'

The Sand-fairy seemed a shade less disagreeable after this.

'It isn't talking I mind,' it said, 'as long as you're reasonably civil. But I'm not going to make polite conversation for you. If you talk nicely to me, perhaps I'll answer you, and perhaps I won't. Now say something.'

Of course no one could think of anything to say, but at last Robert thought of 'How long have you lived here?' and he said it at once.

'Oh, ages – several thousand years,' replied the Psammead.

'Tell us about it. Do.'

'It's all in books.'

'*You* aren't!' Jane said. 'Oh, tell us everything you can about yourself! We don't know anything about you, and you *are* so nice.'

The Sand-fairy smoothed his long rat-like whiskers and smiled between them.

'Do please tell!' said the children all together.

© Rising Stars UK Ltd 2014   *You may photocopy this page*

Name:	Class:	Date:

Geography Lesson

1 Who is the poem about?

_____

AF2

1 mark

2 Which of these patterns describes the rhyming scheme in this poem?
Tick **one**.

ABBA ☐   ABAB ☐   ABCB ☐   AABB ☐

AF4

1 mark

3 Read this line from the poem.

The house he lived in was narrow and grey

Why has the poet chosen to use the phrase *narrow and grey*?
Tick the **best** answer.

The phrase *narrow and grey* fits in with the rhyming scheme. ☐

The poet is describing his teacher's house, which was *narrow* and was *grey* in colour. ☐

The phrase *narrow and grey* has the right rhythm. ☐

The poet is describing his teacher's life, which was limited to a *narrow* range of experiences, and was *grey* and unexciting. ☐

AF5

1 mark

4 The poet's teacher didn't like the British climate.
Find and **copy one sentence** from the poem that tell you this.

_____

_____

AF2

1 mark

/ 4

Total for this page

© Rising Stars UK Ltd 2014   *You may photocopy this page*

5 Look at these lines from the poem.

Then halfway through his final term
He took ill and never returned,
And he never got to that place on the map
Where the green leaves of the orange trees burned.

What do these lines tell you about the poet's teacher?
Write **two** things in your own words.

1 _____

2 _____

AF3
2 marks

6 Draw lines to match each phrase with what it tells you about the poet's teacher.

Phrase	The poet's teacher
the school's stranglehold	failed to make a mark in the world
His name was forgotten	had a vivid imagination
in his mind's eye he could see	felt trapped in his job

AF5
1 mark

7 Read the fifth verse, beginning *The maps were redrawn…*
What point does the poet make in this verse? Tick **one**.

He remembers a lesson his teacher taught him. ☐

His teacher didn't know him very well. ☐

New maps have replaced the old maps his teacher used. ☐

He can't remember his teacher. ☐

AF6
1 mark

/ 4
Total for this page

(8) Why has the poet chosen the title *Geography Lesson*? Tick **one**.

The poem is about a school geography lesson. ☐

The poem is about a lesson the poet was taught about geography. ☐

The poem is about a lesson the poet was taught by a teacher who was interested in geography. ☐

The poem gives the reader a lesson in geography. ☐

[ ] AF6

1 mark

---

(9) The poem is about a lesson the poet learned. What lesson did he learn? Tick the **best** answer.

That there are places where the ocean is glass-clear and blue. ☐

That travelling is fun and educational. ☐

That some people die before they retire. ☐

That you should not put off doing the things you love. ☐

[ ] AF3

1 mark

/ 10

Total for this test

© Rising Stars UK Ltd 2014   *You may photocopy this page*

Name:	Class:	Date:

The Creature in the Sand

1 Draw lines to match each part of the creature's body to its description.

Body part

- ears
- eyes
- body
- hands and feet

Description

- like a monkey's
- like a spider's
- like a snail's
- like a bat's

AF2
1 mark

2 From what you learn in the text, tick to show whether the following are **true** or **false**.

	True	False
The Psammead is thousands of years old.		
The Psammead lives in the gravel pit.		
Psammead is a Latin word.		

AF2
2 marks

3 Read these lines from the text.

'Tell us about it. Do.'
'It's all in books.'
'You aren't!' Jane said. 'Oh, tell us everything you can about yourself!
We don't know anything about you, and you are *so nice.'*

Why does Jane say to the Psammead, *you* are *so nice*?

_____

AF3
1 mark

/ 4
Total for this page

© Rising Stars UK Ltd 2014 *You may photocopy this page*

53

4 The Psammead is vain.

Explain how you know this, using the text to support your answer.

_____

_____

_____

	AF3
	2 marks

5 Look at these sentences that the writer uses in the text.

'Does she always talk nonsense, or is it only the rubbish on her head that makes her silly?'
'So it is to everyone,' said the creature sharply.
'You came to look at me, several sentences ago,' it said crossly, beginning to curl up again in the sand.
'If you talk nicely to me, perhaps I'll answer you, and perhaps I won't.'

Why has the writer included these sentences?

_____

_____

	AF5
	1 mark

6 Number these events to show the order in which they happen.
The first one has been done for you.

☐	Robert asks the creature to stay and talk.
1	The creature insults Jane.
☐	The creature tells the children who it is.
☐	Anthea reassures the creature that they mean it no harm.
☐	The creature is offended because the children don't know who it is.

AF4

1 mark

/ 4

Total for this page

© Rising Stars UK Ltd 2014   *You may photocopy this page*

7 What mood does the writer create in this scene? Tick **one**.

mysterious ☐

amusing ☐

exciting ☐

frightening ☐

AF6
1 mark

---

8 What genre does this text belong to? Tick the **best** answer.

realistic fiction ☐

historical fiction ☐

play script ☐

mystery ☐

fantasy ☐

AF7
1 mark

/ 10
Total for this test

This text is taken from the first chapter of *Kensuke's Kingdom* by Michael Morpurgo.

Kensuke's Kingdom

I disappeared on the night before my twelfth birthday. July 28 1988. Only now can I at last tell the whole extraordinary story, the true story. Kensuke made me promise that I would say nothing, nothing at all, until at least ten years had passed. It was almost the last thing he said to me. I promised, and because of that, I have had to live out a lie. I could let sleeping lies sleep on, but more than ten years have passed now. I have done school, done college, and had time to think. I owe it to my family and to my friends, all of whom I have deceived for so long, to tell the truth about my long disappearance, about how I lived to come back from the dead.

But there is another reason for speaking out now, a far, far better reason. Kensuke was a great man, a good man, and he was my friend. I want the world to know him as I knew him.

Until I was nearly eleven, until the letter came, life was just normal. There were the four of us in the house: my mother, my father, me and Stella – Stella Artois, that is, my one-ear-up and one-ear-down black and white sheep dog, who always seemed to know what was about to happen before it did. But even she could not have foreseen how that letter was going to change our lives forever.

Thinking back, there was a regularity, a sameness about my early childhood. It was down the road each morning to 'the monkey school'. My father called it that because he said the children gibbered and screeched and hung upside down on the climbing-frame in the playground. And, anyway, I was always 'monkey face' to him – when he was in a playful mood, that is, which he often was. The school was really called St Joseph's, and I was happy there, for most of the time, anyway. After school every day, whatever the weather, I'd be off down to the recreation ground for football with Eddie Dodds, my best friend in all the world, and Matt and Bobby and the others. It was muddy down there. Cross the ball

© Rising Stars UK Ltd 2014   *You may photocopy this page*

and it would just land and stick. We had our own team, the Mudlarks we called ourselves, and we were good, too. Visiting teams seemed to expect the ball to bounce for some reason, and by the time they realised it didn't, we were often two or three goals up. We weren't so good away from home.

Every weekend I did a paper round from Mr Patel's shop on the corner. I was saving up for a mountain bike. I wanted to go mountain biking up on the moors with Eddie. The trouble was, I would keep spending what I'd saved. I'm still the same that way.

Sundays were always special, I remember. We'd go dinghy sailing, all of us, on the reservoir, Stella Artois barking her head off at the other boats as if they'd no right to be there. My father loved it, he said, because the air was clear and clean, no brick dust – he worked down at the brickworks. He was a great do-it-yourself fanatic. There was nothing he couldn't fix, even if it didn't need fixing. So he was in his element on a boat. My mother, who worked part time in the office at the same brickworks, revelled in it, too. I remember her once, throwing back her head in the wind and breathing in deep as she sat at the tiller. 'This is it,' she cried. 'This is how life is supposed to be. Wonderful, just wonderful.'

This text is taken from *Why is Snot Green? And Other Extremely Important Questions (and Answers) from the Science Museum* by Glenn Murphy.

Being Human

Ahh – the human body. Forged over millions of years into a finely tuned machine. Incredibly complex and perfectly adapted to its environment, it has allowed us to become the most powerful and intelligent creatures on the planet.

But if you think about it, being human can be pretty gross at times. For all that we've achieved, we still sneeze, burp, fart and poo our way through life. Like huge meaty balloons filled to bursting with snot, gas and worse.

And if our bodies are so clever and complex, how come our eyes go blurry underwater? And how come a blob of ice cream – eaten too quickly – can bring us to our knees?

Here we find out what it *really* means to be human.

> **Why is snot green?**
>
> Basically, because it's the result of a fight between nasty bugs and body cells that make a green-coloured goo.

What?!

Seriously. Snot is made of a sticky substance produced inside the nose that traps and flushes out harmful bacteria. These nasty bugs try to get up your nose when you breathe them in. The sticky stuff stops them getting down your throat and into your lungs, and it also contains cells that your body produces to fight and kill the bugs. It's these that make the green goo. Sneezing and blowing your nose help to clear it all out.

Ugh. Fine. But what do they make the green goo for?

The body cells form part of the incredibly clever and complex defence system in your body. They make special proteins called lysozymes, which help them bust open, eat and digest the bacteria – a bit like the acid in your stomach. For this reason, we call the cells phagocytes, which is Latin for 'eaty-cells' (which you may prefer, but biologists use 'phagocytes' because it sounds more important and clever). It's one of these bacteria-busting proteins that has the green colour.

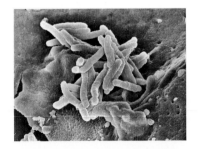

Under the microscope: a phagocyte attacks bacteria

© Rising Stars UK Ltd 2014   *You may photocopy this page*

But why green, and not blue or purple?

This is purely because the protein contains a form of iron that reflects green light and absorbs all the other colours. Incidentally, you find a similar protein in wasabi, the type of horseradish you eat with Japanese sushi, which is why that's green too. Think about that next time you eat horseradish. Or a bogey.

sushi

wasabi

I don't eat bogeys. I don't even pick my nose.

Of course you don't. No one does. No one rolls them up and flicks them, or sticks them under the desk either.

That's right. But if someone did... why would the bogey change colour to dark green, brown or black?

That's because once it's out of its warm, moist home in your nose, the snot begins to dry up as water from it evaporates into the air. When this happens, the phagocytes die and the greenish proteins within them break up – removing the green colour from the bogey.

After this, bacteria in the air settle onto the bogey and start to eat it (waste not, want not, as my mum always says). They chew up all the bits of phagocyte, dead bacteria and skin cells found in the snot, until all that's left is a dried-up mass of brownish-black protein leftovers. And even that gets eaten eventually.

Hang on a minute – how did you know bogeys change colour if you never pick your nose?

Oops.

© Rising Stars UK Ltd 2014   *You may photocopy this page*

Name:	Class:	Date:

Kensuke's Kingdom

1 What did the narrator's father call the school the narrator went to?

_____

AF2
1 mark

- -

2 Look at the first paragraph, beginning *I disappeared…*
What are the **main** points the writer is trying to make? Tick **two**.

He was twelve when he disappeared. ☐

He is ready to tell his story. ☐

He has finished school and college. ☐

He has had time to think. ☐

He owes it to his family and friends to tell the truth. ☐

Kensuke made him promise to wait at least ten years. ☐

AF6
1 mark

- -

3 Draw lines to match each character with something the text tells us about them.

Character	Something about the character
the narrator	was a great man
Stella Artois	played football as a child
Kensuke	loved fixing things
the narrator's father	had a sixth sense

AF2
1 mark

/ 3
Total for this page

© Rising Stars UK Ltd 2014   *You may photocopy this page*

4 Tick to show whether the following sentences about the narrator are **true** or **false**. The first one has been done for you.

	True	False
The narrator is still a child.		✓
The narrator feels loyalty towards Kensuke.		
The narrator was an only child.		
The narrator finds it easy to save money.		
When the letter came, the narrator had a feeling that it would change his life forever.		

AF3

2 marks

5 Look at the final paragraph, beginning *Sundays were always special...*
Find and **copy a phrase** that means the same as 'felt at home'.

_____

AF2

1 mark

6 This text comes from the beginning of a novel. What main purpose do you think the writer had when writing this text? Tick the **best** answer.

to explain the main events of the novel ☐

to introduce the novel's setting ☐

to give the background to the main events ☐

to set the novel's mood ☐

AF6

1 mark

/ 4

Total for this page

© Rising Stars UK Ltd 2014   *You may photocopy this page*

7 *I want the world to know him as I knew him.*
What does this mean? Tick **one**.

The narrator knew Kensuke. ☐

The narrator wishes everyone could have known Kensuke. ☐

The narrator thinks Kensuke should have been famous. ☐

The narrator thinks people misunderstood Kensuke. ☐

AF3
1 mark

---

8 How does the writer create a feeling that something bad is going to happen?
Explain your answer as fully as you can, using the text to help you.

_____

_____

_____

AF5
2 marks

/ 10
Total for this test

© Rising Stars UK Ltd 2014   *You may photocopy this page*

Name:	Class:	Date:

Being Human

1 Why is snot green?
Tick **one**.

One of the bacteria-eating cells in snot is green. ☐

One of the bacteria that snot fights is green. ☐

One of the bacteria-fighting proteins in snot is green. ☐

AF2
1 mark

2 Look at the first section, starting *Ahh – the human body…* and finishing … *what it <u>really</u> means to be human.*

What points is the writer trying to make about the human body? Tick **three**.

The human body has been around for a long time. ☐

The human body is amazing. ☐

The human body is made of meat. ☐

The human body can be disgusting. ☐

The way the human body works can be perplexing. ☐

You shouldn't eat ice cream too quickly. ☐

AF6
1 mark

3 The writer says the human body is *a finely tuned machine.*
What does he mean by this? Tick the **best** answer.

It is temperamental. ☐

It is well balanced. ☐

It works like clockwork. ☐

It performs extremely well. ☐

AF3
1 mark

/ 3
Total for this page

4 Look at the section headed *What?!*
What do you learn about snot from this section? Write **two** things.

1 _____

2 _____

AF2
1 mark

5 Phagocytes need water in order to survive.
How do you know this? Explain as fully as you can, using the text to help you.

_____

_____

AF3
2 marks

6 In this text a lot of the headings are questions. Why do you think the writer chose to do this?

_____

AF4
1 mark

/ 4
Total for this page

© Rising Stars UK Ltd 2014   *You may photocopy this page*

7 In this text the writer characterises snot as both disgusting and useful.

a) **Find** and **copy a phrase** the writer uses to show snot is disgusting.

_____

AF5

1 mark

b) **Find** and **copy a phrase** the writer uses to show snot is useful.

_____

AF5

1 mark

8 What purposes does the writer have for this text? Tick **two**.

to scare   ☐

to inform   ☐

to help   ☐

to instruct   ☐

to amuse   ☐

AF6

1 mark

/ 10

Total for this text

© Rising Stars UK Ltd 2014   *You may photocopy this page*

Answers and mark schemes

Autumn test 1: Part A – The Sword in the Stone

	Part A: *The Sword in the Stone*			AF	Mark	Extra information
1		Fact	Opinion	2	1	Award 1 mark for all three ticks correctly placed.
	Kay has just been knighted.	✓				
	Kay thinks that Arthur is annoying.		✓			
	Kay is older than Arthur.	✓				
2	Arthur will be sent home if he misbehaves. ✓			3	1	
3	Award 1 mark for: • He is cross/angry because he doesn't want Arthur to go with them. Award 1 mark for using appropriate (direct or indirect) reference to the text in support of this, e.g.: • *He tells Arthur he can't go./He says to Arthur, 'You can't go'.* • *'The last thing he wanted was his little brother tagging along behind him.'* • *He protests/says 'But father!' when Ector tells Arthur he can go.*			3	2	
4	[4] Arthur rides ahead to the Blue Boar Inn. [2] Kay tells Arthur he can't go. [5] Ector explains the purpose of the tournament. [3] Ector agrees to let Arthur go. [1] Arthur pleads with his father to let him go to the tournament.			4	1	Award 1 mark for all events correctly numbered.
5	He wants to tell Kay something he doesn't want Arthur to hear. ✓			5	1	
6	A lot of people are going to the tournament. ✓ It may be difficult to find a place to stay. ✓			6	1	Award 1 mark for **both** and **only** these answers ticked.
7	Award 1 mark for each of the following references to the text, provided it is backed up by an explanation, up to a maximum of 2 marks: • *'Arthur was determined not to be left out.'* Determination is an aspect of strong will. • *'It had to be worth just one more try.'* This tells us that Arthur had tried before. This shows perseverance, which is an aspect of strong will. • *'He was already packing his bag.'* This shows how keen and determined Arthur was to go to the tournament. • Arthur doesn't **ask** his father if he should ride ahead; he **tells** him he's going to: *'"I'll go," said Arthur.'*			6	2	
8	a legend ✓			7	1	

© Rising Stars UK Ltd 2014 *You may photocopy this page*

Autumn test 1: Part B – The Titanic

	Part B: *The Titanic*	AF	Mark	Extra information
1	falls — **walls** sea — *gracefully OR eternally* flow — *go* hair — *where*	4	1	Award 1 mark for all three missing words correct.
2	Award 1 mark for each of the following points, up to a maximum of 2 marks: • It is lying at an angle. • It has been taken over by the sea. • It is/was a (very) large ship. • It was a passenger ship/cruise ship (because it had a band).	3	2	Do not accept answers that use wider knowledge rather than answers based on the text.
3	Award 1 mark for one of the following points: • The waves are regular/rhythmical. • The waves are making a (drumming) sound (against the ship). • The waves are moving up and down.	3	1	
4	Award 1 mark for one of the following points: • To make it seem like the shark is taking part in the ghost dancers' dance. • Because the shark is moving gracefully, and dancers move gracefully. • Because the shark is swimming across the ship's ballroom, and the waltz would have been one of the dances danced there. • Because the word *waltzes* alliterates with (begins with the same sound as) the word *white*.	5	1	
5	skeletons clean ✓	2	1	
6	Award 1 mark for any of the following, providing the repeated sounds are underlined: • *Down in the indigo depths of the sea* • *the white shark waltzes gracefully* • *cold shoals flow* • *(and) ghost dancers go* • *(and) ghost dancers go* • *their jewels and beads and bones are tossed* • *into the sand, all turned to stone* • *into the sand, all turned to stone* • *Currents comb their long loose hair* • *Currents comb their long loose hair* • *Under the ocean where water falls* • *the bright fish nibble their glittering bones*	5	1	Do not accept: *as they sing in the sea.*
7	**Phrase** — **The dancers...** their jewels and beads — are dead all turned to stone — have been there a long time and ghost dancers go — are wealthy Their dresses are frayed, their shoes are lost — don't look as good as they once did	5	1	Award 1 mark for all lines drawn correctly.
8	Award 1 mark for any answer referring to the rhythm of the music played by the band and/or the rhythm of the dancers' movements.	6	1	
9	death ✓	6	1	

© Rising Stars UK Ltd 2014   *You may photocopy this page*

Autumn test 2: Part A – The Fire-Maker's Daughter

	Part A: *The Fire-Maker's Daughter*	AF	Mark	Extra information
1	Award 1 mark for one of the following: • In Lalchand's workshop. • In Lila's father's workshop. • In a/the firework-maker's workshop.	2	1	Do not accept: In a workshop.
2	He wants to win the New Year Festival display. ☑	2	1	
3	Award 1 mark for: • She is sure/certain/confident Lalchand will win.	3	1	
4	**Aspect of text** **How it is shown** stage directions — capital letters direct speech — italics characters' names — underlined capital letters scene titles — standard text	4	1	Award 1 mark for all lines drawn correctly.
5	Award 1 mark for one or more of the following points: • The name is a play on words. • 'Puffenflasch' sounds like 'puff and flash'. • 'Puff' and 'flash' are things fireworks do.	5	1	
6	4 A firework goes off. 1 Lila lights a firework. 3 Lalchand burns his fingers. 5 Lalchand asks Lila questions to test her knowledge. 2 Lila tells Lalchand about the poster in the market place.	4	1	Award 1 mark for all events correctly numbered.
7	amusement ☑	6	1	
8	*A rudimentary experiment*	2	1	
9	If the pupil argues that the statement is **true** (i.e. that Lila is ignorant): Award 1 mark for each of the following points, up to a maximum of 2 marks: • She puts too much/a dangerous amount of scorpion oil in a firework. • She doesn't know the ingredients of fly-away powder. • She doesn't know where you find thunder-grains. If the pupil argues that the statement is **not true** (i.e. that Lila is not ignorant): Award 1 mark for one or more of the following points, up to a maximum of 2 marks: • She knows about the New Year Festival display (and/or) the other competitors in the New Year Festival display. • She knows about the secret all firework-makers have to know.	3	2	

© Rising Stars UK Ltd 2014 *You may photocopy this page*

Autumn test 2: Part B – Michelangelo

	Part B: *Michelangelo*	**AF**	**Mark**	**Extra information**
1	biography ☑	7	1	
2	a painter ☑ a poet ☑	2	1	Award 1 mark for **both** and **only** these answers ticked.
3	*It is considered by many experts in art to be a near perfect sculpture.*	2	1	
4	<table><tr><td></td><td>True</td><td>False</td></tr><tr><td>He was born in Florence.</td><td></td><td>✓ (given)</td></tr><tr><td>He was a model student.</td><td></td><td>✓</td></tr><tr><td>He could be argumentative.</td><td>✓</td><td></td></tr><tr><td>Painting was the art form he loved the most.</td><td></td><td>✓</td></tr><tr><td>He was not happy with the Pieta.</td><td></td><td>✓</td></tr></table>	3	2	Award 2 marks for all four ticks correctly placed. Award 1 mark for three ticks correctly placed.
5	He was dedicated. ☑	6	1	
6	Award 1 mark for each of the following points, providing it is backed up by appropriate reference to the text, up to a maximum of 2 marks: • Ghirlandaio recognised how talented Michelangelo was. *Michelangelo's talents became apparent as he worked for Ghirlandaio.* • Within a year of starting his studies with Ghirlandaio, Michelangelo was sent to *work with some of the finest artists... of the time.* • *Michelangelo's fame as a great artist began to grow,* which means a lot of people must have thought his work was exceptional. • *Many people didn't think he could do much with* the piece of marble he chose for his statue of David, but the completed statue *is considered by many experts in art to be a near perfect sculpture.* • The Creation of Adam, a scene from the ceiling of the Sistine Chapel, is *one of the most recreated scenes in all of art and... is one of the most famous paintings in history.*	3	2	
7	**Phrase** **Michelangelo was...** all he wanted to do was... be an artist → uninterested in fame He... wrote over 300 poems → exceptionally talented the only piece of art that Michelangelo signed → single-minded he was hit on the nose... in an argument → hot-headed one of the masterpieces of Renaissance art → creative	5	2	Award 2 marks for all five lines correctly drawn. Award 1 mark for three or four lines correctly drawn.

© Rising Stars UK Ltd 2014 *You may photocopy this page*

Spring test 1: Part A – Prehistoric Britain

	Part A: *Prehistoric Britain*		AF	Mark	Extra information
1	Award 1 mark for: • Around 700,000 years ago.		2	1	
2	**Objects** **Materials** spears — plant stems and leaves rope — animal skins tools — things found nearby clothes — wood shelters — wood, bone and stone		2	1	Award 1 mark for all lines drawn correctly.

3		True	False	3	2	Award 2 marks for all four ticks correctly placed. Award 1 mark for three ticks correctly placed.
	They could not read or write.	✓ (given)				
	They relied heavily on the tools they made.	✓				
	They built permanent settlements.		✓			
	They stayed in Britain throughout the Ice Age.		✓			
	They used clever hunting techniques.	✓				

			AF	Mark	Extra information
4	Award 1 mark for: • The animal would sink into the bog, and wouldn't be able to move.		3	1	
5	Award 1 mark for each of the following points, up to a maximum of 2 marks. • They didn't have fixed homes. • They moved around, following herds of animals. • They slept in caves or shelters. • They had to leave when the cold weather returned/when the animals did.		2	2	
6	report ✓		7	1	
7	The people who lived in Britain during the Ice Age ✓		6	1	
8	in a textbook ✓		7	1	

© Rising Stars UK Ltd 2014 *You may photocopy this page*

Spring test 1: Part B – Carrie's War

	Part B: *Carrie's War*	AF	Mark	Extra information
1	**Word** — **Meaning** unearthly — belonging to the present day brink — priest of an ancient religion contemporary — strange or supernatural sacred — edge of a steep place druid — holy	2	1	Award 1 mark for all lines drawn correctly.
2	She is preoccupied by her thoughts. ☑	3	1	
3	Award 1 mark for one the following points: • Carrie is surprised/amazed/can hardly believe that it has been such a long time. • To Carrie it doesn't seem as long as thirty years ago (since she was last here).	2	1	Do not accept: • It tells you how Carrie is feeling. • It tells you how Carrie speaks. • Carrie is wondering.
4	Award 1 mark for one of the following points: • He doesn't want to get fat. • He doesn't want to be fat like Uncle Nick. • He doesn't want to look like his Uncle Nick.	3	1	
5	Award 1 mark for: • To make them stand out (more) from the characters'/actors' lines/words.	4	1	Do not accept: • To make the text/script easier to read. • To make it clear/obvious they are stage directions.
6	Award 1 mark for any of the following: • To tell us that Carrie's son's dad is dead. • To tell us that Carrie's son's dad was interested in archaeology/history/prehistory.	5	1	Do not accept: • To tell us about Carrie's son's dad.
7	He is unimpressed by it. ☑	5	1	
8a	Award 1 mark for any of the following points, up to a maximum of 2 marks: • The scene starts in darkness. • There are eerie sound effects. • The wind whistles through the trees. • There is an unearthly shriek. • A girl screams. • Carrie shudders. • The stage darkens as the sun passes behind a cloud. • There is a faint rumbling noise of ancient breathing. • Carrie's son mentions ghosts and monsters. • Carrie mentions human sacrifices.	6	2	
8b	Award 1 mark for one of the following points: • When Carrie tells her son he looks a lot like his Uncle Nick, who is fat, her son offers her the rest of the chocolate bar he is eating. • The house is called Druid's Bottom. • Carrie laughs at the name of the house.	6	1	

© Rising Stars UK Ltd 2014   *You may photocopy this page*

Spring test 2: Part A – Barney and the Chalk Pit

	Part A: *Barney and the Chalk Pit*	AF	Mark	Extra information
1	Award 1 mark for any of the following: • A dump. • Things people didn't want. • Strange bits of wreckage. • Moss, elder bushes and nettles. • Something that looked like the steering wheel of a ship. • Something that looked like the tail of an aeroplane. • A bicycle. • A bank of moss.	2	1	
2	Award 1 mark for: *And today was one of those grey days when there was nothing to do, nothing to play, and nowhere to go.* Also allow: *nothing to do, nothing to play, and nowhere to go,* even though it is not a full sentence.	2	1	
3	Award 1 mark for any **two** of the following points: • It is huge. • It was once the side of a hill. • People once dug chalk from it./It was once a chalk quarry. • The quarry operated/people dug for a long time/hundreds of years. • The digging/quarrying has stopped. • People throw things they don't want into it./It is used as a dump.	2	1	
4	Its edge is unstable. ☑	6	1	

5	Award 1 mark for any of the following points, up to a maximum of 2 marks:
	• The writer describes Barney acting cautiously:
	  ○ He *crawls* through the grass rather than walking.
	  ○ He *peers over the edge of the pit.*
	• The writer describes the flints in the side of the pit as being *like bones.* Bones bring to mind skeletons and death.
	• The writer creates a feeling of instability:
	  ○ The writer describes the earth around the edge of the pit as *crumbly.*
	  ○ The writer describes the trees as *holding on desperately by a few roots.*
	  ○ The writer describes things that have already fallen: *The earth and chalk had fallen away beneath them.*
	  ○ The writer predicts that *one day the trees too would fall to the bottom of the pit.*
		5	2	

6	[3] Barney crashes through creepers and ivy. [4] Barney lands on a bank of moss. [2] Barney bumps into a ledge. [5] Barney opens his eyes. [1] Barney turns a somersault.	4	1	Award 1 mark for all events correctly numbered.
7	Award 1 mark for any answer mentioning the bicycle, e.g.: • *He wants the bicycle.* • *He wants to get at the bicycle (and try to mend it).*	3	1	Do not accept any answer that does not specifically mention the bicycle, such as *He wants to play with the junk* or *He wants to explore the dump.*
8	Award 1 mark for any of the following points: • He isn't panicking/scared. • His thoughts are calm/matter-of-fact. • He's never had the ground give way beneath him before. • He's curious/interested in new experiences.	3	1	
9	Barney's thinking was confused. ☑	3	1	

© Rising Stars UK Ltd 2014   *You may photocopy this page*

Spring test 2: Part B – Talking Turkeys

	Part B: *Talking Turkeys*		AF	Mark	Extra information
1			5	1	Award 1 mark for all four missing words correct.

Spelling from the poem	Standard spelling
dem	them
dey	*they*
wid	*with*
mek	*make*
fe	*for*

			AF	Mark	Extra information
2	The poet speaks in a dialect that is not Standard English. ✓		5	1	
3	*'I cannot wait for de chop'*,		2	1	
4			4	1	Award 1 mark for all three words correct and all three ticks correctly placed.

Pair of rhyming words		Full rhyme	Half rhyme
fun	Mum		✓
life	wife	✓	
time	*mind*		✓
please	*trees*	✓	
greens	*beans*	✓	

			AF	Mark	Extra information
5	The poet doesn't like greed. ✓		6	1	
6	Award 1 mark for: *Talking Turkeys* has two meanings: *talking about turkeys* and *turkeys that talk.*		2	1	
7	Turkeys have a right to life. ✓		6	1	
8	Award 1 mark for any of the following points, up to a maximum of 2 marks: • Turkeys like to have fun. • Turkeys enjoy music/reggae/hip-hop. • Turkeys like getting presents. • Turkeys like watching Christmas TV. • Turkeys have mothers. • Turkeys have brains. • Turkeys feel pain. • Turkeys can talk. • Turkeys have/make friends.		3	2	Award 2 marks for three correct points made. Award 1 mark for two correct points made.
9	rhyming verse ✓		7	1	

© Rising Stars UK Ltd 2014   *You may photocopy this page*

Summer test 1: Part A – Geography Lesson

	Part A: *Geography Lesson*	AF	Mark	Extra information
1	Award 1 mark for any of the following points: • The poet's teacher. • One of the poet's teachers. • The poet's geography teacher.	2	1	Do not accept: a teacher.
2	ABCB　☑	4	1	
3	The poet is describing his teacher's life, which was limited to a *narrow* range of experiences, and was *grey* and unexciting.　☑	5	1	
4	*He spoke of the lands he longed to visit,* *Where it was never drab or cold.*	2	1	
5	Award 1 mark for any of the following points, up to a maximum of 2 marks: • He was about to retire. • He (fell ill and) died. • He died shortly before he was due to retire. • He never got to visit the places he wanted. • He died before he could go travelling.	3	2	
6	**Phrase**　　　　　　　　　**The poet's teacher** the school's stranglehold — failed to make a mark in the world His name was forgotten — had a vivid imagination in his mind's eye he could see — felt trapped in his job	5	1	Award 1 mark for all lines drawn correctly.
7	He remembers a lesson his teacher taught him.　☑	6	1	
8	The poem is about a lesson the poet was taught by a teacher who was interested in geography.　☑	6	1	
9	That you should not put off doing the things you love.　☑	3	1	

© Rising Stars UK Ltd 2014　*You may photocopy this page*

Summer test 1: Part B – The Creature in the Sand

Part B: *The Creature in the Sand*	AF	Mark	Extra information
1 **Body part** **Description** ears — like a monkey's eyes — like a spider's body — like a snail's hands and feet — like a bat's	2	1	Award 1 mark for all lines correctly drawn.
2 <table><tr><td></td><td>True</td><td>False</td></tr><tr><td>The Psammead is thousands of years old.</td><td>✓</td><td></td></tr><tr><td>The Psammead lives in the gravel pit.</td><td>✓</td><td></td></tr><tr><td>*Psammead* is a Latin word.</td><td></td><td>✓</td></tr></table>	2	2	Award 2 marks for all three ticks placed correctly. Award 1 mark for two ticks correctly placed.
3 Award 1 point for one of the following points: • She is trying to flatter it/get on its good side/get it in a better mood. • She is trying to persuade it to tell them about itself. • She is trying to get it to do what she wants.	3	1	

4 Award 1 mark for each of the points in the first-level bullets below, providing it is supported by a reference to the text from the second-level bullets. Award a maximum of 2 marks.
 • The Psammead thinks it is important.
   ○ It says, *'Why, you talk as if I were nobody in particular.'*
 • The Psammead can't believe that the children don't know who it is.
   ○ When Jane doesn't recognise the Psammead, it thinks she must either *talk nonsense* all the time, or that her hat is making her *silly*.
   ○ It asks, *'Do you mean to tell me seriously you don't know a Psammead when you see one?'*
   ○ It asks, *'Don't you know a Sand-fairy when you see one?'*
 • The Psammead is upset by the fact that the children don't recognise it.
   ○ *It looked so grieved and hurt...*
 • The Psammead enjoys being flattered.
   ○ When Robert says the Psammead is *much the wonderfullest thing I'd ever seen*, the Psammead cheers up: *The Sand-fairy seemed a shade less disagreeable after this.*
   ○ When Jane says *you are so nice*, the Psammead cheers up even more: *The Sand-fairy smoothed his long rat-like whiskers and smiled between them.*
	3	2	

5 Award 1 mark for: To show that the Psammead is rude/cross/bad-tempered/in a bad mood/grumpy.	5	1	Do not accept: To show what the Psammead is like/to show the Psammead's character.

6 5 Robert asks the creature to stay and talk.
  1 The creature insults Jane.
  4 The creature tells the children who it is.
  2 Anthea reassures the creature that they mean it no harm.
  3 The creature is offended because the children don't know who it is.
	4	1	Award 1 mark for all events correctly numbered.

7 amusing ✓	6	1	
8 fantasy ✓	7	1	

Summer test 2: Part A – Kensuke's Kingdom

	Part A: *Kensuke's Kingdom*	AF	Mark	**Extra information**
1	Award 1 mark for: 'the monkey school'.	2	1	Do not accept: St Joseph's.
2	He is ready to tell his story. ☑ He owes it to his family and friends to tell the truth. ☑	6	1	Award 1 mark for **both** and **only** these answers ticked.
3	**Character** → **Something about the character** the narrator — played football as a child Stella Artois — had a sixth sense Kensuke — was a great man the narrator's father — loved fixing things	2	1	Award 1 mark for all lines correctly drawn.

4		True	False	3	2	Award 2 marks for all four ticks correctly placed.
	The narrator is a child.		✓ (given)			
	The narrator feels loyalty towards Kensuke.	✓				Award 1 mark for three ticks correctly placed.
	The narrator was an only child.	✓				
	The narrator finds it easy to save money.		✓			
	When the letter came, the narrator had a feeling that it would change his life forever.		✓			

		AF	Mark	Extra information
5	*was in his element*	2	1	
6	to give the background to the main events ☑	6	1	
7	The narrator thinks people misunderstood Kensuke. ☑	3	1	
8	Award 1 mark for each of the following points, providing it is backed up by appropriate reference to the text, up to a maximum of 2 marks: • The narrator went missing when he was a child: *I disappeared on the night before my twelfth birthday.* • The narrator suggests that Kensuke is dead: *It was almost the last thing he said to me;* and *Kensuke **was** a great man.* • The narrator suggests that he himself died, or almost died: *I lived to come back from the dead.* • The narrator suggests that a letter would bring important changes to his family's life: *until the letter came, life was normal;* and *even she could not have foreseen how that letter was going to change our lives forever.* • The narrator says he *deceived* his family and friends *for so long* so we know he was hiding something from them/there was something he didn't want them to know.	5	2	

© Rising Stars UK Ltd 2014 *You may photocopy this page*

Summer test 2: Part B – Being Human

	Part B: *Being Human*	AF	Mark	**Extra information**
1	One of the bacteria-fighting proteins in snot is green. ☑	2	1	
2	The human body is amazing. ☑ The human body can be disgusting. ☑ The way the human body works can be perplexing. ☑	6	1	Award 1 mark for **all** and **only** these answers ticked.
3	It performs extremely well. ☑	3	1	
4	Award 1 mark for any **two** of the following points: • Snot is made of a sticky substance produced inside the nose. • Snot traps and flushes out harmful bacteria. • Snot stops bacteria getting down your throat and into your lungs. • Snot contains cells that kill bacteria. • Snot is green because of its bacteria-fighting cells.	2	1	Do not award a mark for mentioning only **one** of the points on the list.
5	Award 1 mark for a correct explanation in the pupil's own words, e.g.: • *When snot is removed from your nose it dries up, and the phagocytes die.* Award a further mark for using an appropriate quote from the text, e.g.: • *… the snot begins to dry up as water from it evaporates into the air. When this happens, the phagocytes die…*	3	2	
6	Award 1 mark for any of the following: • To make the text read like a conversation between the writer and the reader. • To make the tone more 'chatty' and informal.	4	1	
7a	Award 1 mark for any of the following quotes from the text: • *huge meaty balloons filled to bursting with snot, gas and worse…* • *(green-coloured/green) goo…*	5	1	
7b	Award 1 mark for any of the following quotes from the text: • *traps and flushes out harmful bacteria…* • *stops (harmful bacteria/nasty bugs) getting down your throat and into your lungs…* • *contains cells your body produces to fight and kill the bugs…* • *part of the incredibly clever and complex defence system in your body…*	5	1	
8	to inform ☑ to amuse ☑	6	1	Award 1 mark for **both** and **only** these answers ticked.